Jealousy

Graeme Beals

PINNACLE PRESS

Jealousy is the third in a five book series. In trying to attract Tammy's attention away from the big guy to whom she's talking, Tom has an accident - a bad one!

Titles follow in this sequence:

Tom and Tammy – Jealousy
ISBN 9781906125134
Ordering Code – UK7000

Curriculum Concepts UK
The Old School
Upper High Street
Bedlinog
Mid-Glamorgan CF46 6SA

Email: orders@curriculumconcepts.co.uk
www.curriculumconcepts.co.uk

Illustrated by Ross Bennett

Tammy is talking to another boy.

I don't like it.

He is bigger than me.

I don't like him.

Tammy is looking at him.

She is not looking at me anymore.

I am angry.

I try to look like I don't care.

She is still talking to him.

I pretend to read a poster.

She is still talking to him.

I stand where she can see me.

I stretch and yawn so she can see
I am bored.

She keeps on talking to him.

What can I do to get her attention?

Maybe I could punch him?

No - that's not a good idea.

I could just carry her away?

No - that would not be good.

What can I do?

I know, I'm good at making
people laugh.

I'll climb up there.

Then Tammy will see me.

That will make her laugh.

I climb onto the fence.

I let go of the pole.

I pretend I will fall.

I make funny faces.

Suddenly, a motorbike roars past.

I get a fright.

This time I am not pretending.

I fall back onto the road.